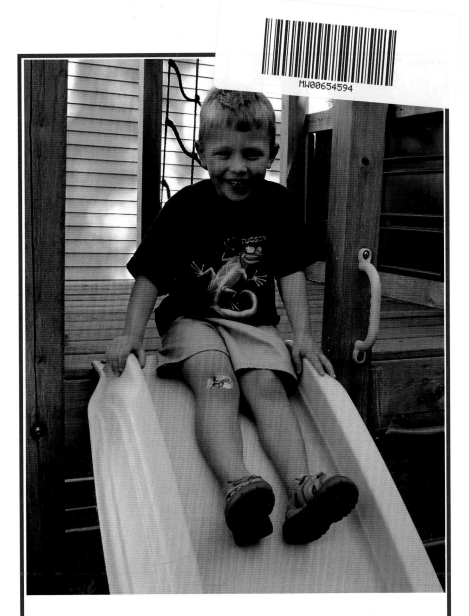

Hi, I'm Ricky. I am 3. I have a food allergy.

peanuts in shell

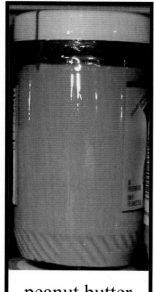

peanut butter

peanuts

I can't eat peanuts or tree nuts. I would get really sick.

cashews

mixed nuts

almonds

trail mix

pistachios

walnuts

Please note: not all tree nuts are shown here.

Lots of foods have peanuts or tree nuts in them, even if you can't see them. They are NOT safe for me to eat.

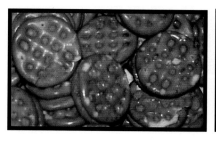

I always ask Mommy or Daddy
before I eat something. At
Nana's house I ask Daddy,
"Is this safe for me?"

Daddy checks it. He says,
"This does not have any nuts
in it. Yes, you can have it."

I can ride my bike to our park. Mommy brings water and snacks.

She also brings my medicine,
just in case I need it. If I ever
feel itchy or sick, I tell Mommy
right away.

I love the swings. Oh, I see candy on the ground.

Big sister Annie yells, "NO! That candy is not safe for you!"

I knew that!

I'm good at soccer. I can run and kick. I go to Annie's games.

Katie has
cereal snacks.
"Want some?" she asks.
"No, I can't share snacks."

I **am** getting hungry.
"Mommy, are the game
snacks safe for me?"

Mommy says, "Yes, I checked them. You may have a bag with Annie."

At Jay's party I ask, "Mommy, is that cake safe to eat? How about the cookies?"

Mommy says, "No, but we packed safe cupcakes for you."

My special cupcakes have lots of icing and sprinkles!

I like going food shopping
with Daddy. I pick out the
apples.

My friend Adam is here! He has cookies. But Daddy says, "No sharing cookies." We don't know if they are safe for me.

19

"Daddy, can I have this?"
Daddy says, "Let me check it.
Yes! That is safe for you."

"Daddy, can I have that candy?" Daddy says, "No, not safe" to some treats I want.

Sometimes, I get really mad.

But I have my own safe treats
that Mommy and Daddy
make for me.

Guess what? Mommy and
Annie just made cookies.

"Can I have a cookie now, Mommy?" Mommy says, "Yes, let's all have cookies!"

Ricky's Quiz for Kids

Parents, these are questions to talk about with your kids. Young children may not yet know the answers. A kindergartener should have correct responses to all of these questions.

Q: Which foods are you allergic to?

Q: If your tummy hurts, or your mouth feels funny, what would you do?
A: Tell a grownup right away.

Q: What would you do if your mouth feels itchy?
A: Tell a grownup right away.

Q: Can you tell if a food is safe just by looking at it?
A: No.

Q: How do you know if a food is safe?
A: Ask Mommy or Daddy. Child may name another trusted adult.

Q: How does Mommy know if a food is safe?
A: Reads the package. Checks the ingredients. Makes it with safe ingredients.

Q: Is it OK to eat from a friend's plate at a party?
A: No, no sharing snacks. My friend might have unsafe food.

Ricky's Party Quiz

Parents, these are party situations to discuss with your older preschooler or kindergartener.

Q: What if Aunt Mo offers you a cookie and tells you she thinks it is safe?

A: I still need to check with Mommy or Daddy.

Q: Your cousin has safe pretzels next to peanut butter crackers on her plate. Can you eat her pretzels?

A: No, no sharing snacks. Daddy says the pretzels may have a tiny bit of peanut butter on them. Daddy can get me some safe pretzels right from the bag.

Q: Your friend's mom forgets you have a food allergy and puts walnuts on your ice cream sundae. If she picks off the walnuts, can you still eat the sundae?

A: No, there could still be traces of walnuts on the sundae. Either Mommy can make me a safe sundae or I can eat my safe party treats.

What Can My Child Eat?

• Always read ingredient labels. Avoid any food containing peanuts or tree nuts.[1]

• Avoid foods that were processed on the same equipment as peanut or tree nut products.

• Call the company if you question whether a food is safe for your child.[2]

• If no ingredients are listed, the answer is "No, you can't have that."

• Be careful of food prepared by others. For example, suppose a friend makes a peanut butter sandwich for her child. Then she uses the same knife to slice an apple for your child. The apple is now **cross-contaminated** with peanut butter. It is not safe for your child.

[1] Download "How to Read a Label" from the Food Allergy & Anaphylaxis Network (FAAN) at www.foodallergy.org. Become an expert label-reader using the tips on this helpful sheet.

[2] The company's phone number should be on the food package. Some companies also have allergen information on their web sites.

First Tips for Parents

• Take a deep breath. You **can** keep your child safe.

• Get a referral to an allergist. An allergist is specially trained to handle your child's serious food allergy.

• Learn the symptoms of an allergic reaction.

• Always carry your child's emergency epinephrine medicine (EpiPen® or Twinject®, for example). Know how to use it.

• With your allergist's help, write down when to use your child's medicine in a Food Allergy Action Plan.[1] Post the plan on your refrigerator.

• Make your home a "safe zone." This means **no** peanut or tree nut products **anywhere** in your home. Your caution will let your child relax at home.

• Tell your extended family and friends about your child's serious food allergy. Begin the job of educating those unfamiliar with food allergies.

[1] Download the Food Allergy Action Plan from the Food Allergy & Anaphylaxis Network (FAAN) at www.foodallergy.org.

Visitors

• Feel free to ask young playmates to wash their hands and faces before playing with your child.

• Remind your relatives and friends of your child's food allergy before they come to visit.

• Ask your visitors not to eat nut products right before visiting. You don't want grandma's hello kiss giving your child hives!

• Even with reminders, your visitors may bring food which is not safe for your child. If the food is store-bought, just check the ingredients. If it is unsafe, politely and firmly explain why you cannot serve it.

• If your visitors bring home-made treats, ask careful questions about the ingredients and preparation. For example, did Aunt Sue make peanut butter cookies at the same time as the oatmeal cookies she brought to your home?

Babysitters

• Before hiring a babysitter to come to your home, make sure he or she understands that your child has a severe food allergy.

• Show your child's babysitter exactly which foods your child may eat.

• Make sure the babysitter understands your child's Food Allergy Action Plan. Train the babysitter to recognize a reaction and to use your child's emergency epinephrine medicine.

• Don't let a babysitter bring unsafe food into your home, even if he or she promises not to share it with your child.

Out and About

• Always take your child's emergency epinephrine medicine with you. If you forget it, go back home and get it.

• Teach your child to ask you before eating anything when out. This may take a while for your child to learn. In the meantime, be vigilant!

• Plan ahead! Always carry a safe snack for your child.

• Bring a safe cupcake or treat for your child if he or she is going to a friend's birthday party.

• If you suspect a party will have bowls of nuts and unsafe snack mixes out, call ahead to see if changes could be made because of your child. If not, you may need to skip the party until your child is older.

• When planning playgroup outings, remind the other parents about your child's allergy. Your child will be safer if your outing does not include peanut butter sandwiches.

• If a young friend does have nut products at a picnic lunch, ask that friend to sit away from your child. Bring plenty of wipes so that friend can have her face and fingers cleaned before playing.

Eating Out

• Fast-food chain restaurants often have menu ingredients listed on their web sites. Check ahead online and also ask at the restaurant.

• Some restaurants will not be safe for your child. Several chain restaurants have peanuts in the waiting area, or serve peanuts as an appetizer.

• Make life easier by calling ahead to see if the chef can provide a safe meal. Ask questions like "What kind of oil do you use when making french fries?"

• Bring extra wipes when eating out. Wipe off your child's table area before he or she sits down.

• Food vendors at fairs and festivals may not know the ingredients in their foods. For special outings, bring a day's worth of safe food for your child.

Preschool Tips

• Start early to look for a safe preschool for your child.

• Visit the school and ask questions about their willingness to work with food-allergic kids.

• Can the preschool maintain a safe nut-free classroom for your child? Does the school provide the snacks? Who brings treats on birthdays? Be willing to share a list of safe snacks.

• Are the teachers trained to recognize an allergic reaction? Are they willing and able to administer your child's emergency medicine? Where would your child's medicine be kept?

• Some craft projects call for peanut and tree nut products. Will the teacher take time to plan ahead and change the craft? Be willing to provide safe substitute foods if you are able.

• Many bird, hamster and dog foods contain peanut and tree nut products. Does the school have pets?

• Download and share helpful teacher resources from Safe@School® Partners at www.foodallergysmart.org.

Learn More

The more you know, the safer your child is! Keep learning through these wonderful groups.

• Contact the Food Allergy & Anaphylaxis Network (FAAN) at www.foodallergy.org. Receive their newsletters and allergy alert messages.

• Join the Kids with Food Allergies group at www.kidswithfoodallergies.org. Learn from other allergy parents through their online forums.

• Join a local food allergy support group. Local groups know the friendliest restaurants and the best nearby allergists. Support group parents can understand your feelings and be there to support you.

• Consider getting a MedicAlert® Bracelet for your child (www.medicalert.org).

• Check back with us at www.safeFoodForMe.com for recommended books on food allergies for kids and adults. We also have updates on Ricky's adventures!